Salo AP47
.99

JOHNNY AND THE MONARCH

By Margaret Friskey

A boy and a dog are confounded
by a butterfly and a disappear-
ing duck. The gay continuity pro-
gresses with simple text supported
by action pictures. The vocabu-
lary of 150 simple words makes
the story easy to read and yet
challenges a reader to do a little
skill building.

Dr. Paul Witty, Director, Psycho-Educational Clinic, North-western University, says: "The Developmental Reading Program is best served by balanced reading which includes a wide variety of self-selection material in addition to basic books. A child's progress is usually most rewarding when his independent reading for fun is guided by teachers, parents, and librarians who strive to help him select books suited to his interests and abilities."

JOHNNY AND THE MONARCH has been classroom tested. Ages 6-8

It has been listed in sixteen states for supplementary or school library use. Among city systems listing it are: Baltimore, Chicago, Tulsa, Cincinnati, New York, Jersey City, Los Angeles, Philadelphia. ALA Booklist.

Skill-builder word list in back of book

Johnny
and the monarch

BY MARGARET FRISKEY · PICTURES BY KATHERINE EVANS

Edited by Illa Podendorf of The Laboratory School of The University of Chicago

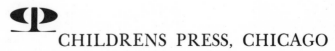
CHILDRENS PRESS, CHICAGO

11 12 13 14 15 16 17 18 19 20 21 R 79 78 77 76

Johnny had a dog named Duke.

He had a duck named Dora.

He lived on a farm at the foot of a hill.

When it was time to hunt for eggs
Johnny went through the woods and across the creek
and up the hill to the hen house.

One day Duke and Dora were going with him
through the woods and across the creek and
up the hill. Dora saw a butterfly on the path.

Dora went after the butterfly.

"Oh, no!" cried Johnny. "The butterfly has hurt his wing." Johnny picked it up and put it on a milkweed plant.

The next day the butterfly was gone. It had left a little yellow-green egg on the milkweed leaf.

Johnny and Duke and Dora watched the egg. One day it hatched into a caterpillar.

The little caterpillar ate the milkweed leaves.
It grew and grew. Its skin became so tight it
split down the back and the caterpillar crawled
out in a new skin. It shed its skin three or
four times before it grew into a big caterpillar.

"No, no!" said Johnny to Dora. "You must not eat the caterpillar. It will turn into a butterfly."

Dora walked away down the creek.
Johnny could not find her.

Every day Johnny and Duke went through the woods
and across the creek and up the hill to look
for Dora. They looked in the chicken yard.
But Dora was not there.

They looked back of the haystack.
But Dora was not there.

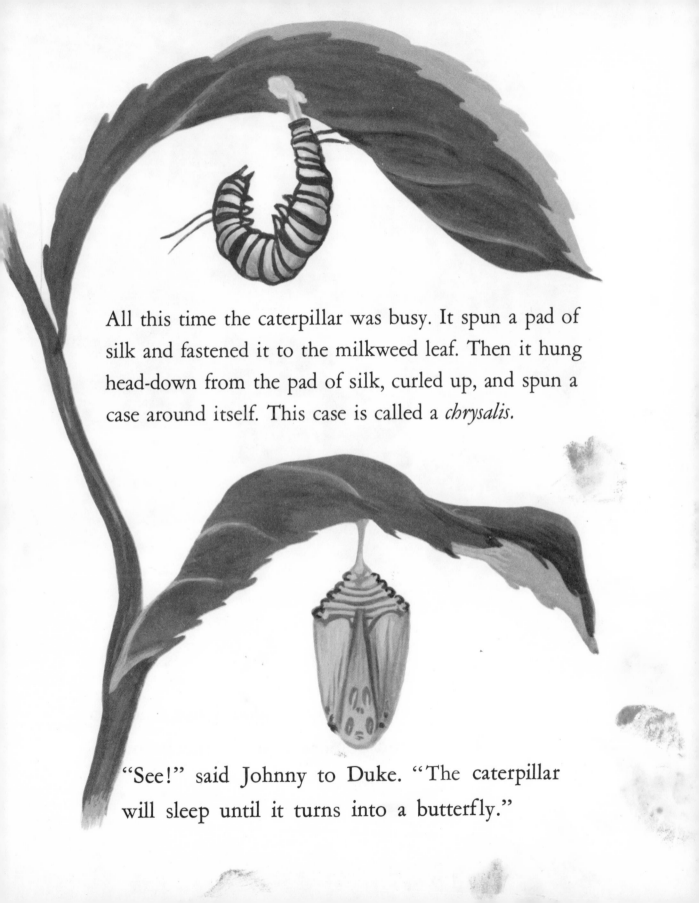

All this time the caterpillar was busy. It spun a pad of silk and fastened it to the milkweed leaf. Then it hung head-down from the pad of silk, curled up, and spun a case around itself. This case is called a *chrysalis*.

"See!" said Johnny to Duke. "The caterpillar will sleep until it turns into a butterfly."

Days went by.

But Johnny and Duke could not find Dora.

They found some kittens in the barn.

They found a wobbly calf.

They found six baby pigs.

They found two baby lambs.

The green chrysalis turned muddy blue.
One day Johnny and Duke went through the woods
and across the creek and up the hill to gather
eggs. The chrysalis was almost black.
"The caterpillar is almost a butterfly," said Johnny.

The chrysalis split open.

A Monarch butterfly with orange and black wings
crawled out on a leaf. The wings were soft.
It could not fly.
The butterfly seemed to pump fluid into its
wings from its body. The wings spread out,
slowly, slowly.
They moved up and down.

Then the butterfly flew off.

"Look at it go!" cried Johnny.

But Duke would not look.

Duke was barking and running up and down the path.

Johnny followed Duke around the bend. There
was Dora coming up the path. Six little
ducklings were following her.

"You had a hidden nest all the time," said Johnny.

Johnny put the ducklings in his egg basket.
Then Johnny and Duke and Dora and the six
little ducklings went down the hill and across
the creek and through the woods and home.

WORDS I CAN READ IN THIS BOOK

*Skill-builders (not in the First Thousand Words for Children's Reading). Sound out, or get meaning from the sentence or the picture.

a
across
after
all
almost
and
around
at
ate
away

baby
back
barking
barn
basket
because
before
bend
big
black
blue
body
butterfly
busy
by

calf
*caterpillar
chicken
*chrysalis
coming
could
*crawled
creek
cried
*curled

day
dog
*dots
down
duck
*ducklings

eat
eggs
every

*fastened
find
flew
fly
*fluid
followed
found
four
from

gather
go
gold
gone
green
grew

had
has
*hatched
*haystack
he
head
hen
her
*hidden
him
his
home
house
hung
hunt
hurt

in
into
it
*itself

kittens

lambs
leaf
leaves
left
little
lived
look

*milkweed
moved
*muddy
must

named
nest
new
next
no
not

of
off
oh
on
one
open
or
orange
out

*pad
path
picked
pigs
plant
*pump
put

*running

said
saw
see
seemed

shed
*silk
six
skin
sleep
slowly
so
soft
some
*split
*spun

the
then
there
they
this
three
through
*tight
time
to
turn
two

until
up

walked
was
watched
went
were
when
will
wing
with
*wobbly
wood
would

yard
yellow
you